Drums Notation Explained

DRUM VOICES
The drums are arranged
around the staff as follows.

1. Kick drum	**6.** Buzz Snare	**11.** Hi hat closed
2. Floor tom	**7.** Medium tom	**12.** Hi hat open *
3. Snare drum	**8.** High tom	**13.** Crash cymbal *
4. Rim shot	**9.** Ride cymbal *	**14.** Hi hat (foot)
5. Ghost snare	**10.** Ride cymbal on bell *	**15.** Hi hat open (foot) *
		16. Hi hat (foot) and kick drum together

* For clarity, all cymbals,
regardless of rhythmic value,
ring on unless specifically
marked as choked.

General Musical Notation

 (accent)
- Accentuate note (play it louder).

Fill
- Ad lib. section played around the kit, often at the end of a section.

 (accent)
- Accentuate note with great intensity.

- Repeat bars between signs.

Choke

- After striking either the crash or the ride cymbal, grasp the cymbal rim to prevent it from ringing on.

- When a repeated section has different endings, play the first ending only the first time and the second ending only the second time.

D.%. al Coda
- Go back to the sign (%), then play until the bar marked ***To Coda*** ⊕ then skip to the section marked ⊕ ***Coda***.

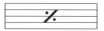
- Repeat previous bar. In higher grades these may also be marked *sim.* or *cont. sim.*

D.C. al Fine
- Go back to the beginning of the song and play until the bar marked ***Fine*** (end).

- Repeat previous 2 bars. In higher grades these may also be marked *sim.* or *cont. sim.*

Roof Down

Peter Huntington

♩=90 *Hip Hop*

© 2006 Rock School Ltd.

This music is copyright. Photocopying is illegal.

Better Drums With...

Rockschool

www.rockschool.co.uk

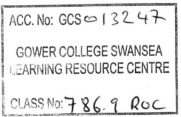

Welcome To Debut Drums

Welcome to the Rockschool Debut Drums pack. The book and CD contain everything needed to play drums in this grade. In the book you will find the exam scores in standard notation. The accompanying CD has full stereo mixes of each tune, backing tracks to play along with for practice, one with a click and one without for each song, and spoken two bar count-ins to each piece. Handy tips on playing the pieces and the marking schemes can be found in the Guru's Guide on page 14. If you have any queries about this or any other Rockschool exam, please call us on **0845 460 4747**, email us at *info@rockschool.co.uk* or visit our website *www.rockschool.co.uk*. Good luck!

Entry Level Techniques In Debut

The nine Rockschool grades are divided into four levels. These levels correspond to the levels of the National Qualifications Framework (NQF). Further details about the NQF can be found at *www.qca.org.uk/NQF*. Details of all Rockschool's accredited qualifications can be found at *www.qca.org.uk/openquals*.

Debut Drums is part of the Entry Level. This Level is for players who are just starting out and who are looking to acquire the basic skills of performing.

Debut: in Debut Drums you will be concentrating on playing tunes. A player of Debut standard should be able to play up to 20 bars of music in 4/4 time, using simple grooves composed of quarter and eighth notes and associated rests. The hi hat remains closed at all times during the pieces. There are occasional simple fills found at the end of some of the four bar patterns.

Drums Exams at Debut

There are **two** types of exam that can be taken using this pack: a Grade Exam and a Performance Certificate.

Debut Drums Exam: this is for players who want to develop performance and technical skills

Players wishing to enter for a Debut Drums exam need to prepare **three** chosen from the printed repertoire. In addition you must prepare the technical exercises in the book, undertake a sight reading test, take an ear test and answer general musicianship questions. Samples of these tests are printed in the book along with audio examples on the CD.

Debut Drums Performance Certificate: this is for players who want to focus on performing in a range of styles

To enter for your Debut Drums Performance Certificate you play pieces only. You can choose any **five** of the six tunes printed in this book.

You can find more information on the Debut Drums exam in the Guru's Guide on page 14.

Punk Funk

Adrian York

♩=93 *Modern Funk*

Debut Drums

5

Little Miss Meg

Deirdre Cartwright

Be Cool

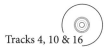

Noam Lederman

Alabama

John Murphy

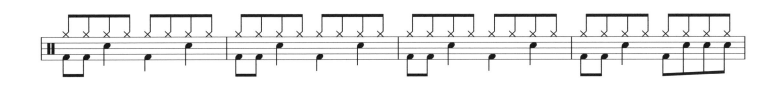

Debut Drums

© 2006 Rock School Ltd.

This music is copyright. Photocopying is illegal.

Grade Exam and Performance Certificate Entry Form

Please complete the form below in BLOCK CAPITALS. Information given below will only be used by Rockschool for exam purposes and for Rockschool news. Completed application forms should be sent, along with a cheque made payable to 'Rockschool' for the appropriate fees, to:

Exam Entries, Rockschool, Evergreen House, 2-4 King Street, Twickenham, Middlesex, TW1 3RZ

1. Candidate's Details

Full Name (as it will appear on the certificate):

Date of Birth (DD/MM/YY)*:   Gender (M/F)*:   *This information is compulsory but will be used for statistical purposes only

Address:

Postcode:

Telephone No: Mobile No:

Email address:

☐ (Please tick) **Yes!** I would like to receive all correspondence from Rockschool via email (with the exception of certificates and mark sheets which will be posted). *Rockschool will NOT circulate your email address to any third parties.*

2. Your Examination

Type of Exam (Grade or Performance Certificate):   Grade:

Instrument: *If you are applying for multiple examinations, please continue below:*

| Type of Exam: | Instrument: | Grade: |
| Type of Exam: | Instrument: | Grade: |

Period (A/B/C)*:   *Refer to our website for exam periods and closing dates*

Preferred Town for Examination (*Refer to our website for a list of current towns with Rockschool examination centres*)*:

Rockschool will endeavour to place you at your preferred town, but cannot guarantee this

Please state any dates that are IMPOSSIBLE for you to attend*:

It is not guaranteed that we can avoid these dates

3. Additional information

Drum Candidates. Do you require a left-handed kit?

Will you be bringing your own kit (Grades 6,7,8 only)?   If 'no' Rockschool will provide a drum kit.

Popular Piano Candidates. Will you be bringing your own keyboard?

If 'no', Rockschool can provide either a keyboard or a piano. Please indicate which you prefer :

Special Needs Candidates. Please include a supporting letter with your application explaining your requirements.

All Candidates. If there is any additional information you consider relevant, please attach a note to your application.

4. Fees – *For current exam prices please refer to our website, www.rockschool.co.uk or call us on 0845 460 4747*

Fee enclosed:

Cheque Number: PLEASE WRITE CANDIDATE NAME ON BACK OF CHEQUE

Teacher's Exam Entry Form

Teachers wishing to enter **grade exams** and **performance certificates** on behalf of their students should complete the form below in BLOCK CAPITALS. Information given will only be used by Rockschool for exam purposes and for Rockschool news. You can get up to date information on examination prices from **www.rockschool.co.uk** or by ringing the Rockschool helpline on **0845 460 4747**. Completed application forms should be sent, along with a cheque made payable to '**Rockschool**' for the appropriate fees, to:

Exam Entries, Rockschool, Evergreen House, 2-4 King Street, Twickenham, Middlesex, TW1 3RZ

1. Teacher's Details

Title (Mr/Mrs/Ms etc):	Full Name:
Address:	
	Postcode:
Telephone No:	Mobile No:
Email address:	
For school entries please include your NCN (National Centre Number):	

☐ (Please tick) **Yes!** I would like to receive all correspondence from Rockschool via email (with the exception of certificates and mark sheets which will be posted). *Rockschool will NOT circulate your email address to any third parties.*

2. Examination Details and Fees

*For grade exams, please write 'G' and the grade number in the Grade box (e.g. **G6** for Grade 6). For performance certificates, please write 'PC' and the grade number in the Grade box (e.g. **PC4** for Performance Certificate Grade 4). †For examination periods refer to our website. Continue on separate sheet if necessary.* FOR SPECIAL NEEDS CANDIDATES PLEASE ATTACH A SUPPORTING LETTER WITH DETAILS.

Candidate's Name (as it will appear on the certificate)	Date of Birth	Gender (M/F)	Instrument	Grade*	Period†	Fee (£)
1.	DD MM YYYY					
2.	DD MM YYYY					
3.	DD MM YYYY					
4.	DD MM YYYY					
5.	DD MM YYYY					
6.	DD MM YYYY					
7.	DD MM YYYY					
8.	DD MM YYYY					
9.	DD MM YYYY					
10.	DD MM YYYY					
11.	DD MM YYYY					
12.	DD MM YYYY					
				Total fees enclosed £		

Preferred Town for Examination (*Refer to our website for a list of current towns with Rockschool examination centres**):

*Rockschool will endeavour to place your candidates at your preferred town, but cannot guarantee this

Please list dates your candidate(s) **cannot** attend*:

*It is not guaranteed that we can avoid these dates

Band Exam Entry Form

You can enter for one of the following band exams (1 Guitar player, 1 Bass player, 1 Drummer) using Rockschool materials: *Level One (Grade 3 repertoire) * Level Two (Grade 5 repertoire) *Level Three (Grade 8 repertoire)* Please complete the form below in BLOCK CAPITALS. Information given will only be used by Rockschool for exam purposes and for Rockschool news. Completed application forms should be sent, along with a cheque made payable to 'Rockschool' for the appropriate fees, to:

Exam Entries, Rockschool, Evergreen House, 2-4 King Street, Twickenham, Middlesex, TW1 3RZ

---

1. Band's Details

GUITARIST Full Name (as it will appear on the certificate):

Date of Birth (DD/MM/YY)*:   Gender (M/F)*:

BASSIST Full Name (as it will appear on the certificate):

Date of Birth (DD/MM/YY)*:   Gender (M/F)*:

DRUMMER Full Name (as it will appear on the certificate):

Date of Birth (DD/MM/YY)*:   Gender (M/F)*:

*This information is compulsory but will be used for statistical purposes only

---

2. Band's Main Contact Details

Main Contact's Name:

Address:

Postcode:

Telephone No: Mobile No:

Email address:

☐ (Please tick) **Yes!** I would like to receive all correspondence from Rockschool via email (with the exception of certificates and mark sheets which will be posted). *Rockschool will NOT circulate your email address to any third parties.*

---

3. Your Examination — *If you are applying for multiple exams, please use a separate form for each*

Exam Level (One/Two/Three):

Period (A/B/C)*:   *Refer to our website for exam periods and closing dates

Preferred Town for Examination (*Refer to our website for a list of current towns with Rockschool examination centres*):

*Rockschool will endeavour to place you at your preferred town, but cannot guarantee this

Please state any dates that are IMPOSSIBLE for you to attend*:

*It is not guaranteed that we can avoid these dates

Additional Information *If there is any additional information you consider relevant (e.g. band members with special needs) please attach a separate sheet explaining your requirements.*

---

4. Fees — *For current exam prices please refer to our website, www.rockschool.co.uk or call us on 0845 460 4747*

Fee enclosed:

Cheque Number: PLEASE WRITE CANDIDATES' NAMES ON BACK OF CHEQUE

ROCKSCHOOL HELPLINE: 0845 460 4747
email: info@rockschool.co.uk   website: www.rockschool.co.uk

ROCKSCHOOL RESOURCES

At Rockschool we recognise the importance of keeping teachers and learners up to date with developments. Below are listed the qualifications and resources on offer. If you have any questions, please contact us through the relevant email address, or phone us on **0845 460 4747**.

PERFORMANCE DIPLOMAS

Music Performance Diploma
(DipRSL Perf) at Level 4

Music Performance Licentiate
(LRSL Perf) at Level 6

The Rockschool Performance Diplomas provide flexible, vocationally relevant qualifications for experienced or skilled performers of popular music.

diplomas@rockschool.co.uk

TEACHING DIPLOMAS

Teaching Diploma
(DipRSL) at Level 4
Teaching Diploma
(LRSL) at Level 6

The Rockschool Teaching Diplomas have been devised for instrumentalists, vocalists and music technologists who would like to attain a teaching qualification without having to attend a course or write essays. The diplomas focus on the practicalities of teaching and are neither genre nor instrument specific.

diplomas@rockschool.co.uk

MUSIC PRACTITIONERS QUALIFICATIONS

Rockschool/ATM
14-19 Diploma
Compatible

These flexible, vocationally relevant popular music qualifications will provide learners with the necessary skills to develop realistic employment opportunities in the music industry.

qualifications@rockschool.co.uk

COMPANION GUIDES

Sight Reading (Grades 1-8)
Improvisation & Interpretation
(Grades 1-5)
QSPs (Grades 6-8)
Ear Tests (Grades 1-8)
GMQs (Grades 1-8)

A must for any music teacher or self-taught musician using the Rockschool grade system. Rockschool Companion Guides contain examples of the exercises you will encounter in an exam along with tips on how best to perform.

info@rockschool.co.uk

Companion Guides available for purchase through **www.musicroom.com**

GUITAR DVDS

Following DVDs available:
Grades Debut & 1
Grade 2
Grade 3

Perfect for anyone working through the Rockschool grades, Rockschool DVDs include instructional lessons on how to make the most of the pieces and technical exercises required in your exams.

info@rockschool.co.uk

DVDs available for purchase through **www.musicroom.com**

COMING SOON...REPERTOIRE BOOKS

Rockschool Repertoire Books contain popular songs from rock through to indie. **Drums Grades 1 to 3** will be available from October 2008.

info@rockschool.co.uk

Repertoire Books soon available for purchase through **www.musicroom.com**

13 Daze Late

Luke Aldridge

♩=88 *Soul*

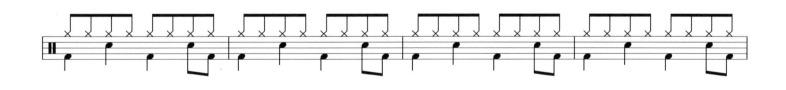

Technical Exercises

In this section, the examiner will ask you to play a selection of exercises drawn from each of the four groups shown below. In addition there is a fill exercise which you will play using the designated backing track on the CD. You do not need to memorise the exercises (and can use your book in the exam) but the examiner will be looking for the speed of your response. The examiner will also give credit for the level of your musicality.

The stickings shown (L & R) are there as a guide for right handed drummers. Left handed drummers should reverse the sticking patterns. Groups A–D should be played at ♩ = 70.

Group A: Single Strokes

1. In eighth notes

Group B: Double Strokes

1. In eighth notes

Group C: Paradiddles

1. Standard paradiddle in eigth notes

Group D: Fill

In the exam you will be asked to play the three bar groove shown below followed by one of the notated fills chosen by the examiner. You will perform this exercise in the exam to the backing track on the CD.

Sight Reading

Printed below is the type of sight reading test you are likely to encounter in the exam. The piece will be composed in the style of either rock or blues. The examiner will allow you 90 seconds to prepare it and will set the tempo for you on a metronome. The tempo is ♩=60.

Rock

Ear Tests

There are two ear tests in this grade. The examiner will play each test to you on CD. You will find one example of each type of test you will be given in the exam printed below.

Test 1: Fill Recognition

The examiner will play you one bar of snare drum fill twice on a CD and you will then be asked to play it back. You will then be asked to identify the fill from the two printed examples shown below. The tempo is ♩ = 70.

Test 2: Groove Recall

The examiner will play you a two bar drum groove repeated on a CD twice. You will be asked to play back the groove as you have heard it on the CD. The tempo is ♩ = 80.

General Musicianship Questions

You will be asked five General Musicianship Questions at the end of the exam. The examiner will ask questions based on pieces you have played in the exam. Some of the theoretical topics can be found in the Technical Exercises.

Topics:

i)   Music theory
ii)   Knowledge of your instrument

The music theory questions will cover the recognition of the following at this grade:

Drum voices on the stave
Note values

The instrument knowledge questions will cover the following topics at this grade:

Names and position of all drum voices

Questions on all these topics will be based on pieces played by you in the exam. Tips on how to approach this part of the exam can be found in the Rockschool Companion Guide and on the Rockschool website: *www.rockschool.co.uk*.

The Guru's Guide To Debut Drums

This section contains some handy hints compiled by Rockschool's Drums Guru to help you get the most out of the performance pieces. Do feel free to adapt the tunes to suit your playing style. Remember, these tunes are your chance to show your musical imagination and personality.

The stickings shown in the music are suggestions only. Feel free to use different sticking combinations as they suit you. Please also note that any solos featured in the full mixes are not meant to be indicative of the standard required for the grade. The track listings below are grouped: 1-16: full mixes; 7-12: backing tracks without clicks; and 13-18: backing tracks with clicks.

Debut Drums Tunes

Rockschool tunes help you play the hit tunes you enjoy. The pieces have been written by top pop and rock composers and players according to style specifications drawn up by Rockschool.

The tunes printed here fall into two categories. The first category can be called the 'contemporary mainstream' and features current styles in today's charts. The second category of pieces consists of 'roots styles', those classic grooves and genres which influence every generation of performers.

CD full mix track 1, backing tracks 7 & 13: Roof Down

A groove in a hip hop style. The first four bars of this song have an off-beat eighth note kick drum pattern and a tricky fill in bar 4. Thereafter, the pattern is laid out for eleven bars with a variation of the fill in bar 4 in the very last bar. The tempo at 90 beats per minute is quite laid back so try to play the pattern evenly.

Composer: Peter Huntington.

CD full mix track 2, backing tracks 8 & 14: Punk Funk

In this modern funk piece you are counting out four to the bar with the hi hat throughout the song, apart from the last bar. The groove features off-beat eighth note kick drums and a kick-snare combination that will require concentration to play correctly. The groove in bars 1-4 is repeated in bars 9-12. The fill in the last bar is played with both hands (snare and hi hat) and the kick drum foot.

Composer: Adrian York.

CD full mix track 3, backing tracks 9 & 15: Little Miss Meg

This 60s style surf rock piece is played on the hi hat in eighth notes for most of the piece, apart from the fills at the end of bars 4, 8, 12 and 17. The groove pattern laid down in the first four bars (three bars of groove and a bar of fill in the last bar of four) is maintained for twelve bars but note the variations to the pattern in the third set of four bars. Make sure that you count the rests in bar 17 so that the last two bars are played in time with the CD.

Composer: Deirdre Cartwright.

CD full mix track 4, backing tracks 10 & 16: Be Cool

This is a rock piece with a familiar rock groove alternating quarter and eighth notes on the kick drum. The first four bars are repeated in the next three after which there is a fill with an alternating snare and kick drum pattern played in eighth notes. The second half of the song features an eighth note kick drum pattern with variations. Make sure to practice the pattern in the last two bars, particularly the kick drum as it is quite intricate.

Composer: Noam Lederman.

CD full mix track 5, backing tracks 11 & 17: Alabama

At 80 beats per minute, this is the slowest of the songs in this set, so make sure that you play in a strict tempo and resist the temptation to rush the groove. The eighth note hi hat pattern is laid down for the whole song apart from the last bar, and the groove is propelled forward by the eighth note kick drum figures. There are some tricky snare-kick variations to this pattern in bars 7, 8 and 15 which will need attention.

Composer: John Murphy.

CD full mix track 6, backing tracks 12 and 18: 13 Daze Late

This modern soul piece has a groove featuring an off-beat eighth note kick drum played for the first eight bars with fills at the end of each set of four. The tempo is relaxed so make sure that you play this as evenly as you can. The groove switches to a different kick drum pattern for the next five bars followed by a break in bar 14 where you will need to count the rests before the main groove theme returns for the last two bars.

Composer: Luke Aldridge.

CD Musicians:

Guitar: Deirdre Cartwright
Bass: Henry Thomas
Drums: George Gavin
Keyboards and programming: Alastair Gavin

Debut Drums Marking Scheme

The table below shows the marking scheme for the Debut Drums exam. Please note that all successful candidates will be certificated as achieving a pass only.

ELEMENT	PASS
Piece 1	13 out of 20
Piece 2	13 out of 20
Piece 3	13 out of 20
Technical Exercises	11 out of 15
Sight Reading	6 out of 10
Ear Tests	6 out of 10
General Musicianship Questions	3 out of 5
Total Marks	**Pass: 65%+**

The table below shows the marking scheme for the Debut Bass Performance Certificate. Please note that all successful candidates will be certificated as achieving a pass only.

ELEMENT	PASS
Piece 1	14 out of 20
Piece 2	14 out of 20
Piece 3	14 out of 20
Piece 4	14 out of 20
Piece 5	14 out of 20
Total Marks	**Pass: 70%+**

Entering Rockschool Exams

Entering a Rockschool exam is easy. Please read through these instructions carefully before filling in the exam entry form. Information on current exam fees can be obtained from Rockschool by ringing 0845 460 4747 or by logging on to our website *www.rockschool.co.uk*.

- You should enter for your exam when you feel ready.

- You can enter for any one of three examination periods. These are shown below with their closing dates.

PERIOD	DURATION	CLOSING DATE
Period A	1st February to 15th March	1st December
Period B	1st May to 31st July	1st April
Period C	23rd October to 15th December	1st October

These dates will apply from 1st September 2006 until further notice

- Please complete the form giving the information required. Please fill in the type and level of exam, the instrument, along with the period and year. Finally, fill in the fee box with the appropriate amount. You can obtain up to date information on all Rockschool exam fees from the website: *www.rockschool.co.uk*. You should send this form with a cheque or postal order (payable to Rockschool Ltd) to the address shown on the order form. **Please also indicate on the form whether or not you would like to receive notification via email.**

- Applications received after the expiry of the closing date may be accepted subject to the payment of an additional fee.

- When you enter an exam you will receive from Rockschool an acknowledgement letter or email containing a copy of our exam regulations.

- Rockschool will allocate your entry to a centre and you will receive notification of the exam, showing a date, location and time as well as advice of what to bring to the centre. We endeavour to give you four weeks' notice of your exam.

- You should inform Rockschool of any cancellations or alterations to the schedule as soon as you can as it is usually not possible to transfer entries from one centre, or one period, to another without the payment of an additional fee.

- Please bring your music book and CD to the exam. You may not use photocopied music, nor the music used by someone else in another exam. The examiner will sign each book during each examination. You may be barred from taking an exam if you use someone else's music.

- You should aim to arrive for your Debut exam fifteen minutes before the time stated on the schedule.

- Each Debut grade exam is scheduled to last for 12 minutes. Each Debut performance certificate is scheduled to last 10 minutes.

- Two to three weeks after the exam you will receive a copy of the examiner's mark sheet. Every successful player will receive a Rockschool certificate of achievement.